THE GHOSTLY TALES

OF

CAPE COD

Published by Arcadia Children's Books
A Division of Arcadia Publishing
Charleston, SC
www.arcadiapublishing.com

Spooky America is a trademark of Arcadia Publishing, Inc.

First published 2022

ISBN 9781540252210

Library of Congress Control Number: 2022932060

All images courtesy of Shutterstock.com; p. 16 Shanshan0312/Shutterstock.com;
p. 26 J.A. Johnson/Shutterstock.com.

Spooky America

THE
GHOSTLY TALES
OF
CAPE COD

KAREN BUSH GIBSON

Adapted from *Haunted Cape Cod* by Barbara Sillery

arcadia
CHILDREN'S BOOKS

VT   NH

MASSACHUSETTS

CT   RI

CAPE COD

TABLE OF CONTENTS & MAP KEY

Introduction

When people hear the name "Cape Cod," they often think of sandy beaches and summer vacations. But this sandy peninsula jutting into the Atlantic Ocean like a crooked arm is more than that. It is where Colonial America begins. And numerous ghosts have been left behind.

The Wampanoag people were early Cape Cod residents. They lived and fished on this coastal land during the spring and summer months. When the weather turned cold, they moved inland for protection from the icy winds coming off the ocean.

The Wampanoag lived this way for thousands of years. But in 1620, a group of people known as Pilgrims arrived in large wooden ships at the tip of the peninsula. These people from England were looking for a new home, but they soon decided that Cape Cod wasn't it. The land was too sandy for farming and livestock. As soon as they were able, the Pilgrims sailed across the bay. They settled there and named their new home Plymouth. Plymouth is part of the mainland, not the Cape Code peninsula.

***

Even though the Pilgrims didn't stay on Cape Cod, many others did settle there. By 1639, people had settled on the peninsula, creating towns like Sandwich, Barnstable, and Yarmouth. They farmed and hunted. And like the Wampanoag before them, they fished.

With the number of residents who have lived in this area over the past four hundred years, it's not surprising that some never left. Different theories explain why ghosts remain in a place. One is that this is their home, the place they were happiest. Other theories point to some type of trauma, like that experienced by Goody Hallett, which keeps them in a place. Goody Hallett walks Marconi Beach on dark and stormy nights, forever looking for her pirate love, Sam Bellamy. Bellamy lost his life in 1717 when his ship, the *Whydah Gally*, sank off the coast in a storm.

Sometimes, a disturbance activates ghostly activity. Such a disturbance happened in 1909, when digging for a new canal began. It apparently annoyed seven people buried in the nearby Sagamore Cemetery, and they have made themselves known to paranormal investigators. They are known to be unhappy ghosts.

These are just some of the ghosts who haunt Cape Cod. And in this book, you will meet more of the best-known spirits who still call this place home. From Native American princesses to early settlers and British soldiers. There are glass artisans, innkeepers, and even cats.

The Yankee ghosts that reside on Cape Cod are said to be every bit as stubborn as their real-life counterparts. They may think their identity is none of your business, thank you very much. And they'll just continue to rattle windows, move chairs, let the dogs out, shoot an icy breeze your way, and block doors.

We don't always know the identity of the ghosts. We look for clues in the history of a place. Who lived there? And more importantly, who died there? Was the death peaceful or was there some unfinished business that keeps a spirit tied to a place?

If you're very lucky, Cape Cod ghosts will allow you a brief glimpse. Until then, they prefer to keep you guessing.

The House of Puzzles

In 1637, Sandwich was the first town established on Cape Cod. It is bordered by the bay on one side and the marshlands on the other. The residents found that they could easily use the marsh grass as hay for their livestock. Within two years, about sixty Pilgrim families had settled in Sandwich. Quaker families joined them by the late 1600s.

The John Pope House, located in the village

of Sandwich, is reminiscent of Hogwarts from *Harry Potter*. Odd staircases, secret rooms, and plenty of surprises. The original Colonial-style home was built on a hill overlooking a salt marsh and the Mill River.

Nothing much surprises current owners Jana and Bix Hamby anymore. The house not only has disappearing stairs, doors to nowhere, and secret passageways; it also seems to have a few ghosts.

The home was built by Seth Pope for his son, John, and his family in 1699. It has five sections or bays. The home was sold to Joseph and Mehitable Nye in 1749. Joseph made additions to the home, doubling its size.

***

Their son, Joseph Nye Jr., made his own modifications during the American Revolution, including an escape route in the house. The largest of the upstairs bedrooms contains a secret panel next to the fireplace. Through it, Nye could quickly make his escape from either the first floor or the cellar.

In 1913, the home was turned into Tupper Inn. To accommodate travelers, the upstairs bedrooms were divided into 10 tiny rooms. It's unknown whether there are any guests who never checked out.

The Hambys have worked on restoring the home to its former glory. When they first visited the house before buying it, a couple of friends came with them. Jana and another woman climbed the back staircase. The friend felt like she was being followed. She called out to her husband to see if it was him, but the men were at the other end of the house.

When they learned the history of the house, the woman became convinced that Seth Pope's ghost was behind her on that staircase.

That night, she dreamed that Seth Pope was walking in the marsh, happy that someone was moving in to the grand home he built so long ago.

Strange noises are common in the house. Jana explains this as floors and walls settling with changes in temperatures. With the additions made by the Nyes in the 1700s and the renovations through the years, it's as if the home is struggling with being joined.

Likewise, the Hambys don't think there are any supernatural forces that cause the windows to slam shut with enough force to take off fingers. Jana explains that her "guillotine windows" just need special blocks to hold them up.

***

Jana has explanations for the many oddities of her home, and none of them involve ghosts.

She doesn't believe in them. However, many others have no doubt that multiple ghosts reside in this home.

The most common ghostly sighting at the John Pope House has been of a woman with pale blue eyes. She has been seen both outside the house by people driving by and inside a bedroom known as the Twin Chamber.

A couple of years ago, a man came and knocked on their door. Jana could see that he looked a little shaken. "He said he saw this pale woman in a white cap and tattered gray dress swooping up the lawn. Her feet did not touch the ground."

The man reported that the ghost ran past an old hitching post to the side of the house, where she disappeared at a locked side door. The key for the door was lost long ago. Inside the door, a decaying lace curtain covers the upper glass pane. The outside door just stops. It doesn't lead anywhere inside the house.

On the same wall inside the house is a closet in the dining room. For some reason, the right side of the closet contains four steps that disappear into the wall. Where did these steps lead?

Jana believes that the Twin Chamber was once a children's room. A rocking chair sits on a two-foot-high platform next to a window. Perhaps a good place for a mother to sit and rock while watching over her sleeping children? A few people who have slept in the room report having awakened to find the blue-eyed ghost sitting on the bed and watching them.

**

One theory is that the female ghost is Elizabeth Pope, the wife of John and mother to six children. Elizabeth died when her youngest child, Mary, was a toddler. It is believed that Elizabeth returns to check on her children.

Although not seen as often as the adult woman ghost, neighbors have reported seeing a small girl looking out an upstairs window. Could it be young Mary looking for her mother?

When the house was still an inn, a young couple were guests. They had a "ghost finder" app on their tablet, which told them that there were ghosts in an upstairs bedroom and a common room downstairs. The app couldn't tell them whether the ghosts were Popes, Nyes, or perhaps someone else, but it confirmed that some spirits still lived in the house.

Do the secret rooms and passageways have anything to do with the ghostly presences? As the Hambys continue their discoveries and renovations, perhaps a few more surprises await them.

SANDWICH
GLASS
MUSEUM
of the
SANDWICH
HISTORICAL
SOCIETY

SHOP
MUSEUM STORE
ANYTIME

GLASSBLOWING
DAILY

The Glassmakers Ball

It is said that magic happens once a year in the Jarvesville Historic District of Sandwich. When evening comes, watch and listen carefully. On this night, the anniversary of the Glassmakers Ball, you may hear the sounds of fiddles. Keep watch for a phantom parade that supposedly takes place. It is led by a slender, dashing figure with a glass ruby star pinned to his chest and a golden glass cane in his hand. You might even hear the sighs of female ghosts admiring the handsome figure.

The ghost is followed by two more spirits, overly confident old men who don't seem to realize that they aren't the stars of this show. That all eyes aren't on the graceful figure in front of them.

This leader occasionally appears as transparent as glass. He stops to rap his glass cane on various doors before continuing his stroll down the street, just like he's done for more than 150 years, marking the anniversary of the Glassmakers Masquerade Ball.

***

The Jarvesville Historic District of Sandwich grew up around the Boston and Sandwich Glass Factory. The factory was founded in 1825 by Boston businessman Deming Jarves and was largely responsible for the town's growth.

It changed the town from a quiet farming village to an industrial town. The glass factory consisted of the buildings where the glass was made, as well as housing for the workers.

Boston and Sandwich glass wasn't like the glass in windows or mirrors. This was glass used for dining ware, drinking glasses, and decoration. It was beautiful and elegant. By the 1850s, the Boston and Sandwich Glass Factory was one of the largest producers of glassware in the country. Its five hundred workers produced more than five million pieces of glass each year.

Examples of the glass were on display in the windows of homes and shops. It was customary at the time to hang glass witch balls in windows to stop evil spirits, spells, and disaster from entering the building.

Village boys worked at the Sandwich factory as rosin monkeys and mold boys. Rosin monkeys tossed ground-up bits of rosin into the furnace to keep the fire going. Mold boys used iron tongs to remove glass molds from the fire.

All the boys had the opportunity to learn the craft of glassmaking as apprentices. They could train to become chipmasters, workers who chipped flakes of glass off of the openings of the glassware. And if they were really good, they could become master glassblowers, known as gaffers.

***

Deming Jarves hired the best gaffers from all over Europe in order to bring the "spirit of glass" to the factory. The best of these was a man named Adolphe Bonique. Little was known about Bonique other than that he was from France.

Because Bonique didn't talk about himself, two chipmasters began to invent stories about him. They told the young apprentices that Bonique was the son of a nobleman who escaped the guillotines of the French Revolution just in time. Another story suggested that Bonique had been Napoleon's right-hand man when it came to planning military strategy. And another rumor suggested that Bonique was a rich descendant of one of the Acadian families who had escaped persecution in Canada.

What couldn't be denied was Bonique's skill as a glassblower. The boys whispered that he cast spells on the glass. How else could he create a glass bell that rang by itself each hour or a glass flower that opened when the sun shone on it? Bonique denied that he was the creator of these magical items. But if not him, then who?

Each year, Deming Jarves held the Glassmakers Masquerade Ball to celebrate the workers. The entire community would create costumes for the ball. Women wore gowns with glass flowers sewn onto them. Men would dress in new breeches and coats. One year, everyone attended the ball except for Bonique. Bonique rarely socialized and was said to be extremely shy around women. He was seen fleeing to the woods outside of town before the ball started.

The ball was a success. People were dancing and enjoying the party. Suddenly, a masked stranger appeared in the middle of the dance floor. He was dressed elegantly in a white silk coat with a glass ruby star pinned on a blue ribbon across his chest. This masked stranger bowed to the ladies and left the room. Then he disappeared.

As the two chipmasters walked home after the ball in the wee hours of the morning, they spotted the stranger. They watched as he rapped gently at a few doors with his gold glass cane. Who was he looking for?

The next day, the glassworkers appeared at the glass factory a little more tired than usual but happy after having had a good time at the ball. They talked about the stranger who had suddenly appeared on the dance floor. People whispered it must have been Bonique hidden behind a mask. Bonique admitted to nothing.

There were also whispers that Bonique's true identity was supernatural. Perhaps he was a shape-shifter. By day, he could make magic with glass. And one night a year, he used his magic to shapeshift into an immortal phantom for the Glassmakers Masquerade Ball.

Today, nothing remains of the Boston and Sandwich Glass Factory. It stopped operations on New Year's Day 1888. Later owners tried to restart it without success. The buildings were torn down in the 1920s and 1940s.

All that remains of the glass factory is a simple concrete block at the corner of Factory

and Jarves Streets. On it is a bronze plaque that pays tribute to the "glass factory that built a town" along with a raised map of the factory. And of course, the ghostly parade of the Glassmakers Masquerade Ball. If you're very quiet, perhaps you'll hear the chatter of two old men spinning their tales of the master gaffer.

Haunted Highfield

Highfield Hall sits high on a hill in Falmouth on the southern coast of Cape Cod. Its 157 windows look out over the property and occasionally provide the careful observer a glimpse of previous residents who either won't or can't leave. And there are apparently quite a few of them.

When the railroad arrived in Falmouth in 1872, it transformed the quiet fishing community into a popular summer destination for the rich. One of those families was the Beebes, who once lived on a hill in Falmouth. They were a family plagued by tragedy who left their mark on this Cape Code hilltop.

James Madison Beebe had seven children. Two died as young adults, while a third lost her husband just two years after marriage. After James's death, his remaining sons built grand mansions on seven hundred acres of land their father had purchased. The land looked out over the town of Falmouth. Pierson and Frank Beebe built an almost eighteen-thousand-square-foot mansion that they named Highfield Hall in 1878. They lived there with sister Emily.

***

Another brother, J. Arthur Beebe, built a similar mansion farther up the hill a year later.

He named his home Tanglewood. The woods between the two homes became known as Beebe Woods. The Beebes enjoyed entertaining. Family and friends, not to mention gardeners and house staff, very often made their way from one house to another through the woods. When they were in residence, it wasn't uncommon to see both homes on the hill lit up, with the sounds of music drifting down over the town.

J. Arthur and Emily Beebe lost their son to suicide in 1900, and Emily remained inconsolable up until her death in 1911. J. Arthur worried for his daughter, also named Emily. She had lost her mother and brother, and he tried to distract her with trips abroad. But Emily tragically took her life shortly thereafter. When J. Arthur heard the news, he ordered his chauffeur to race to his daughter's side. Horribly, the chauffeur struck and killed a ten-year-old boy who was crossing the street. J. Arthur died of heart failure two years after his daughter, but some say he died from a broken heart.

While dealing with family tragedies, J. Arthur Beebe had allowed the Tanglewood estate to fall into disrepair. After his death, the remnants of the once magnificent house high on a hill looked every bit the haunted house. In his will, J. Arthur left Tanglewood to Harvard University. The college was unable to find a buyer, so it rented the house out.

Moses Sloat Fassett Hodgson stayed here as a boy one summer with his grandmother. He recalls doors often opening by themselves. Their response was to speak to the resident ghost, believed to be J. Arthur Beebe. "When this occurred . . . it was custom to say, politely, 'Come in, Mr. Beebe.'"

**

It is said that Highfield Hall has several ghosts. One of its former residents is a woman who hovers over the staircase. Another wears a long brown dress and rushes down a hallway. An elderly male is seen on the third floor. A young girl peers through the upstairs railing to watch guests dancing in a holiday ball long ago. Spirits wander around the grounds and have been seen in the barn.

People commonly believe that at least one of the female ghosts is Emily Beebe. But since the original Beebe sister as well as the wife and daughter of J. Arthur were all named Emily, it's difficult to know which one of them haunts the hill. The old man is likely one of the Beebe men, perhaps J. Arthur.

By 1947, the Beebe homes became part of a theater complex. The Highfield Hall barn was transformed into a theater known as the Highfield Playhouse. The females lived dormitory style in the Tanglewood mansion. The males lived on the third floor of Highfield Hall.

One of the women who used to perform at the theater has seemingly decided she's not ready to give up her role. She is called Faye, although no one is certain if that is her name. She likes to slam theater seats open and play boisterous music on the piano. She turns lights on after you've turned them off. And she scatters makeup along the hallways. Occasionally, Faye even makes an appearance.

She once appeared in front of a set designer, telling him that she used to live here.

It's not only the buildings that hold spooky tales. In the winter of 1962, ornithologist Frank N. Whitman disappeared in woods that he had hiked in for over sixty years. It would be another ten years before his bones were found. A cause of death was never discovered. Others have also found themselves lost in the Beebe woods. Fortunately they did not suffer the same fate as Frank N. Whitman.

With no one willing to save Tanglewood, it finally came to its end with a wrecker's ball on May 20, 1977. Highfield Hall remained standing but was abandoned as all of the Beebe siblings had died. As the house deteriorated, lights would flash on and off. An alarm system often summoned the police to the house, but no one was ever found on the grounds. It became known as "the spooky house on the hill where phantom music played."

In 1994, it looked like Highfield Hall might suffer the same fate as Tanglewood, but a group of citizens came together to save it. They

volunteered to clean it up, and they spread the word about how important it was to save the once grand house. Eventually, their message was heard. In 2000, the town took ownership.

The following year, the home was leased to a nonprofit group, Highfield Hall & Gardens, which has turned it into a cultural center.

The Beebe family must be happy that one of their homes survived and is bringing joy to other people now.

A Revolutionary Time

The Crocker Tavern was built in 1754 on the Old King's Highway in Barnstable. The Old King's Highway started as a Native American trail and trade route, but it soon became a major thoroughfare in Cape Cod. Crocker Tavern soon became a popular stage coach stop.

America was on the verge of war at that time. Each night, tavern owner Cornelius Crocker dealt with customers whose emotions were running high. Many customers were colonists who believed in independence from England. But sometimes, British soldiers or Tories, colonists loyal to England, entered his establishment. Debate was common. Often, arguments broke out. Fists sometimes flew as well.

Although Crocker was a Tory, business always came first. His daughter, Lydia, watched everything, and as she grew older, she helped her father run the tavern. When he died, she took over its operations.

Lydia was more sympathetic to the patriots. Crocker Tavern became known as Aunt Lydia's Tavern among the colonists. After hours, Aunt Lydia's Tavern was the meeting place for Whigs, colonists seeking independence. In 1774, they were plotting their freedom from British rule. One of those Whigs was James Otis Jr., known as Cape Cod's first patriot.

According to Samuel Adams and President John Adams, Otis was instrumental in America winning its independence.

One day by accident, a British soldier walked into a Whig meeting in the barn on the Crocker property. Swords were quickly drawn, and a fight broke out. During the thrusting and jabbing, the soldier got his sword stuck in a beam. Unable to pull it out, he soon fell victim to a patriot's sword.

Since then, people report having encounters with the ghost of this British soldier. One woman on a ghost tour thought she was watching a guide in a Revolutionary War–era costume. She later learned there were no employees in costume. And the notch in the beam where his sword was stuck can still be seen.

In the inn, another soldier has been seen walking across one of the bedrooms. This ghost is believed to be an American soldier, a member of the Cape Cod militia who gathered in front of the tavern to march to Lexington and Concord.

Another guest reported being in bed with her husband when she realized another man—a ghost—was lying on her other side. She woke her husband, but when they both turned to the third person in the bed, he had vanished.

Although several ghosts have been reported, Aunt Lydia is believed to be the most active ghost at the Crocker Tavern. She has made her presence known in many ways.

During a renovation, doors were open as workmen carried in furniture. Without even the slightest wind, the back door slammed shut. Not only did it shut, but the eye and hook latched to lock the door. The owner tried to re-create this strange event without success. The owner finally admitted that it must have been Lydia's doing. Even in death, Lydia makes sure that the doors are closed and locked. She is obviously keeping unwanted guests out.

Aunt Lydia's bedroom is reported to have the most paranormal activity in the house. She has appeared to numerous guests who have slept in her old room. She appears as an elderly woman dressed in a colonial-type gown and bonnet. As she stands over the bed, she watches guests sleep. Other times, although she can't be seen, she lets you know she's there by giving the bed a violent shake.

Several people have reported hearing a woman's voice shout, "Help me! Help me!" coming from the inside of the house. A search never reveals anyone in distress. Is the woman

Aunt Lydia or is it someone else? Perhaps a guest who ran into some trouble? We may never know who this spirit in distress is.

After the American Revolution, Lydia turned the Crocker Tavern over to her daughter Sally. She served drinks there until 1837. The place remained a popular tavern for decades but was eventually turned into a private residence. The building stayed in the Crocker family until 1927. Since then, it has operated as a museum, bed-and-breakfast, and vacation rental.

Crocker Tavern is located in the Old King's Highway Historic District. As the largest historic district in the nation, it stretches across Cape Cod from Sandwich to Orleans.

Barnstable refers to its stretch of the Old King's Highway as Main Street. Many nearby buildings on Main Street also date back to the seventeenth century. They include the Old Colonial Courthouse, Village Schoolhouse,

Sturgis Library, and Old Gaol (the British word for jail).

Built in 1690, the Old Gaol is reported to be the oldest wooden prison in the United States. The cells have had the same iron bars, hinges, and locks for more than three hundred years.

Although it hasn't been used as a jail since 1820, it appears that some prisoners or perhaps their jailers have never left. Look carefully. Is that a shadowy figure moving around the first floor? And there! It's now standing by a ladder that leads to the second floor where the jail cells were located.

Paranormal investigators say two of the former prisoners doomed to be jailed forever are known as Joel and Mary. We don't know who they are or why there were in jail. But whatever their crimes, they are doomed to spend eternity in Barnstable's Old Gaol.

The Ghosts of
Barnstable House

Barnstable is one of fifteen towns that make up Cape Cod. It is the largest and stretches the width of the peninsula, with Cape Cod Bay bordering the north and Nantucket Sound on its south shore.

The town was first settled by the British in 1639. Initially, farmers and shipmasters made their home here. When the railroad arrived in

1854, it brought more trade and business to the town.

And although Crocker Tavern is well-known for its spooky inhabitants, it was far from the only place in the town of Barnstable with ghosts. Barnstable House is reported to be the home of eleven different ghosts.

The two-story colonial home was owned and probably built by James Paine, the grandfather of Robert Treat Paine, a participant at the signing of the Declaration of Independence. The home was actually built in Scituate, just south of Boston, in 1713. It was then floated by barge to Barnstable in 1716. James Paine had the house placed on a foundation built over an underground river. A hole in the cellar allowed the Paine family to lower a bucket in the river to get water for bathing, cooking, and cleaning.

Sadly, the first ghost who appeared is also the youngest. Six-year-old Lucy was said to be playing in the cellar. She was chasing after her favorite blue ball when she fell into the river and drowned. In life, Lucy was a happy child, and it appears that she is a happy ghost too. Giggles and the sound of a bouncing ball let you know that Lucy is playing nearby. Sometimes she shows herself, her brown curls bouncing as she runs and plays.

A chair by the fireplace occasionally rocks by itself. People have also reported seeing flames flare up, then disappear in the fireplace. This is believed to be Bethia Paine, Lucy's mother, rocking by the fireplace and mourning the loss of her daughter.

Another shadow is seen around the property, but it never appears in the house. This is said to be Edmund Hawes, who bought the home from the Paines. After he unexpectedly lost his entire fortune, he hanged himself from a tree near the house.

Dr. Samuel Savage bought the Paine house in the late 1700s. Although he made his living as a doctor, it is said that he liked to dabble in the supernatural. He reportedly knew how to open a door to the spirit world. People came to his home to hold seances and talk to the spirits of people who had passed away.

Neighborhood children were said to dread walking past Dr. Savage's house. When not working, he often sat on his porch. If you passed his house without removing your hat or curtsying, you were sure to earn his wrath. It is believed that Dr. Savage may still be around, just waiting to yell at mannerless children who pass by.

Captain John Grey lived in the house during the mid-1800s. He was reportedly a grouchy man, but not much is known about his life except that a devoted servant was always by his side. In the 1950s, about one hundred years after Captain Grey lived here, the owners decided to turn the house into an inn and named it after him—Captain Grey's Inn. This apparently didn't sit well with Captain Grey. He interrupted dinners by yanking off the tablecloth, flipping chairs over, and dropping water pitchers.

Captain Grey's Inn was renovated and renamed Barnstable House. This seemed to calm Captain Grey, because he hasn't made an appearance since the inn was renamed. Apparently, all he wanted was to be left alone.

However, the staff at Barnstable House regularly bumped into a man in a yellow, double-breasted jacket and breeches. He would bow and wave them on. No one seems to know who this ghostly presence is.

In the 1970s, a fire broke out at Barnstable House one snowy evening. Firefighters arrived

to find smoke pouring out of the third-story attic windows. Suddenly, a woman with long blonde hair and dressed in a white nightgown appeared at the window. The firefighters rushed to her rescue, but she seemed to disappear.

After the fire was out, one of the firemen was wrapping up the hose. A young woman in a nightgown and no coat approached him. He was about to suggest that she put on something warm since it was a very chilly night. But then he looked down at her feet. It wasn't the fact that they were bare that surprised him as much as the fact that they weren't touching the ground. She was levitating!

As this ghost hadn't been seen before the fire, one wonders if something about the fire disturbed her and brought her spirit out in the open. Locals refer to her as Martha. They look for her in the upper windows or floating from the ghostly flames to the ground.

By the 1980s, the restaurant had closed, and Barnstable House was converted into office space. A new restaurant, the Barnstable Restaurant and Tavern, opened up in the center of town. The owner purchased some of the furniture from Barnstable House. The furniture must have had some connection to Lucy, because she's been spotted at the new restaurant too. She often tugged on the uniform of a waitress she liked. No doubt, Lucy wanted to play. When the waitress told Lucy she was too busy to play, Lucy disappeared—for a time.

Every once in a while, Lucy turns up again at Barnstable House Restaurant and Tavern in search for a playmate. A man who rented office space on the second floor of the building claims to have seen a little girl with brown hair and a blue dress waiting on the stair landing several times. She would grin before running down the hall and disappearing.

If you get a chance to visit Barnstable, be prepared to see some ghosts, because there certainly are a lot of them around!

The Extraordinary Bookstore

Old bookstores can be magical places for book lovers. When you step inside, it's like you are suddenly on a treasure hunt. You don't know what the treasure is, but you'll know it when you find it. It's the unexpected and unknown that holds so much promise in a bookstore. The Isaiah Thomas Rare Book Store in Cotuit takes that one step further. Because it's not only books that provide the unexpected and unknown.

Some of the unexpected is thanks to the owner. The shocking pink Victorian exterior. A Shakespeare bust wearing Mickey Mouse ears. A large one-eyed teddy bear in pink traditional German breeches sitting on the couch in the children's section.

Then there are the otherworldly things that can't really be explained. Like the pendulum clock that hangs on a wall. The circular brass pendulum swings back and forth, keeping time with a tick-tick-tick. Although the clock is battery operated, the pendulum seems to have a mind of its own. When bookstore owner Jim Visbeck returned from a trip one time, the pendulum stopped the moment he entered the store. This has happened multiple times when Jim returns to the bookstore.

Before you begin to wonder whether the clock is reacting to being left alone, know that the pendulum has also stopped during certain conversations. Particularly conversations related to whether the clock is haunted or not. It's as if the clock wants to listen in on conversations.

Sometimes, things go crashing in the bookstore. It's hard to pin on the store's cats when they're not around. And in one case, a framed sketch would have had to jump over a small brass statue in front of it before crashing to the floor.

And the supernatural happenings don't just happen in the bookstore. Jim and his partner live upstairs above the bookstore. More than once, Jim has felt a depression at the foot of his bed, as if someone has sat down. And on one occasion, when Jim walked past the sofa, he had to do a double take. An older woman with gray hair and a high-collared dress sat there. When he looked a second time, she had vanished. A neighbor believes this was likely the wife or one of the daughters of the original owner.

The original owner was Zenas Crocker III. After he had made his money in the California Gold Rush, he built the home in 1861. (It's unknown whether he was related to the Crockers who operated the Crocker Tavern. There have been Crockers in Cape Cod since its earliest days.)

Jim bought the building in 1989. Before he transformed it into a bookstore, it had been many things, including a women's clothing store, a salon, a real estate office, and a funeral home. And parts of it had been used as private apartments and offices.

Jim has a photograph of the Crocker family that hangs in the bookstore. Zenas stands next to his wife, Susan, and two sons, Zenas IV and Frances. Standing apart from them are two daughters, Hattie and Helen.

During renovations to the building, Jim discovered some interesting things. Like a small set of stairs near a fireplace that

reach a single room at the top of the house. The door to the room had a peep hole and a latch on the outside. When he opened the door, he discovered that the room was lined with mattresses.

Jim had heard rumors that one of the women in the Crocker family suffered from mental illness. Was Susan, Hattie, or Helen at one point locked in that mattress-lined room? Was it one of their ghosts that was now forever confined to the house?

When word got out that the Isaiah Thomas Rare Book Store was haunted, Jim had former occupants visit with stories of their own. A couple of nursing students lived here for a month one summer. Funny things kept happening. And not so funny things. One of the roommates reported that she was pushed down the stairs by unknown forces.

With over 70,000 books, there are many secrets in the Isaiah Thomas Rare Book Store, and some of them aren't found in the books. Jim wasn't a believer in the supernatural at first, but too many things have happened for him to dismiss it any longer. Still, he's turned down offers from Hollywood because he doesn't want the place to be known as the "haunted bookstore." Jim believes that if he just shows a little respect to the ghost, they can co-exist just fine. And it seems to be working—so far.

Ye Old Yarmouth Inn

Established in 1696, the Old Yarmouth Inn in Yarmouth Port is Cape Cod's oldest inn—and it has a lot of history. It is midway between Plymouth, at the start of the cape, and Provincetown, at the end of the cape. So it was the perfect place for many weary travelers to stop on their journey for lodging, food, and drink. Revolutionary War soldiers were rumored to have been stationed here.

And the inn was reported to be a stop on the Underground Railroad before the Civil War.

Present owners Sheila FitzGerald and Arpad Voros believe that the spirits of some of the people who passed through the door of Ye Old Yarmouth Inn are still hanging around. They don't know who most of those ghosts are, but there is one whose identity they are sure of: Bradford Powell.

One evening, Sheila was working at the hostess stand in the restaurant. The front door had been left open. Before she could close it, a rotund man walked by. He wore an old-fashioned suit, a shirt with fancy cuffs, and black boots. Sheila had never seen a ghost before, but she was pretty sure that was what had just walked by her. He definitely wasn't from the present.

Sheila isn't the only one to have seen Bradford Powell's ghost. Many people have claimed to have seen him making his way around Ye Old Yarmouth Inn. In every reported sighting, the description of his appearance has been the same: he is about five feet, eight inches tall, a bit round, and has a crown of white, fluffy hair and a jowly face.

So how do the owners know their ghost by name? Soon after Sheila and Arpad took over Ye Old Yarmouth Inn, they met a woman named

Althea Davis, who was ninety-eight years old at the time. She told them that her grandfather Bradford Powell used to live in the house, and she shared some pictures of him with the new owners. The man in the photographs was the spitting image of their ghost.

Bradford Powell was a dentist who had his practice in the downstairs rooms, while the family lived upstairs. The Powells rented out the spare bedrooms to local schoolteachers.

When Althea was a little girl, she was playing upstairs one day and discovered a secret room built between the fireplaces. She opened some of the closets and fell down behind the chimney. Luckily, one of the teachers heard her screams and rescued her.

Later, this very same teacher died in the house, supposedly from smoke inhalation from the wood-burning fireplace. It is believed that this teacher had a romantic relationship with Bradford.

Sheila believes that the ghost of this teacher refused to leave the house. She only appears on the second floor, and Sheila says, "She is not nearly as nice as Bradford. She's like the scary ghost and more of a troublemaker."

Once, some friends came to visit Sheila and Arpad. The next morning, Sheila discovered one friend downstairs with his bags packed and ready to leave. Sheila says, "I asked him if everything was OK. 'You're not leaving until tomorrow.' He looked at me and said, 'I'm not spending another night here.' Naturally, I asked him why."

The friend reported feeling as if someone was sitting on the bed next to him at bedtime.

He couldn't see anyone, so he dismissed it as a dream. Then, someone started tickling his feet, but no one was there. It's hard to dismiss your feet being tickled as a dream. The man pulled the covers over his head and told himself that if one more thing happened, he was leaving. And just then, it was as if someone grabbed the bedposts and started shaking the bed, banging it on the floor.

Other antics are common at the Old Yarmouth Inn. Odd noises. Windows shaking. Glasses that move along the bar in the restaurant. Money dropped near the old wood stove being sucked up into it. One morning, Sheila's sister came downstairs to start some coffee, and the mixer started up by itself.

Instead of real candles, Sheila and Arpad use safe, rechargeable lights that look like candles in the main dining room. One Sunday morning, candle wax was discovered on a white table cloth and across the rug. It looked as if someone had carried a candle, and the wax dripped along the way. The owners questioned staff and looked around. No one had lit a real candle, and no candles could be found.

But one of the strangest episodes involved the owner's dogs. One night when they were getting ready to close up and go home, Arpad found their two dogs outside on the upper deck. He checked to see if someone had let them out. No one had.

Ye Old Yarmouth Inn has security cameras, and Sheila and Arpad decided to review the security video. And they couldn't believe what they saw.

In the video, they watched Indi, a Lab-hound mix, walk down the hall. She stopped at the door to the outside. It looked like she did a little play bow. Then Indi turned around and wagged her tail at the wall before walking down the hall. Several minutes later, Indi ran back down the hall and out the door, which was now somehow open.

About twelve seconds later, Wheezie, a basset hound–Lab mix, ran down the hall and outside. The door closed behind her. Wheezie has a reputation for barking at everyone and everything not familiar, but she didn't make a sound during this entire incident.

The security video didn't reveal any ghosts, but it certainly showed a supernatural occurrence. The dogs were responding to something. What, we don't know. It's unlikely Indi and Wheezie will ever tell, but perhaps the ghost of one of the many people who spent time at Cape Cod's oldest inn will.

The Haunted Café

The Troutman brothers bought a restaurant in the small town of Dennis in 1987. Located less than a mile from Scargo Lake, it seemed only natural to name the restaurant Scargo Café, especially after hearing the legend of Princess Scargo.

The legend says that Princess Scargo was the lovely daughter of a Nobscussett chief. She met a Wampanoag warrior and fell in love. The warrior promised to return, but until then, he left her with a hollowed-out pumpkin filled with four shiny fish.

The fish outgrew their home and were released into a spring. However, the spring began to dry up. The Nobscussett people dug a fish-shaped lake with clamshells, and Princess Scargo filled it with her tears. The fish multiplied. Soon afterward, the warrior returned and married Princess Scargo. They lived happily ever after by the lake.

The Troutmans wanted to honor the legend and the town's history by making the café a success. But what they didn't realize was that there was a ghostly presence working against them. Five previous owners had tried and failed with restaurants at this location. It was as if the location was cursed. Based on the Troutmans' first three years of operation, it appears that the failures may have been the result of a mean-spirited ghost.

The dining areas are all downstairs. The second floor was used for offices, storage, and

changing rooms for the staff. The brothers noticed that the staff preferred changing in a downstairs bathroom. They heard complaints that it felt creepy upstairs, as if someone was watching them change clothes. Other staff whispered about hearing heavy breathing or being poked in the back.

A waiter once went upstairs to get a highchair from the storage area. He felt hands on his back, shoving him hard down the stairs. He caught his balance and turned around, but he didn't see anything. There was talk that the

angry spirit was a disturbed young man named Junior who had lived in the house in the 1950s. And no one wanted to go upstairs because of Junior.

Although Scargo Café is open year-round, its busiest time is in the summer. This is when the Troutmans hire extra help, usually college students, for the summer season. As the third summer came to a close, one college student said her good-byes and took off down the Mid-Cape Highway. After she returned home, she called the café to tell the Troutmans the frightening experience she had gone through.

The young woman was very uneasy for much of the drive. It felt like someone was in the backseat of her car. But she couldn't see anyone when she turned around or when she looked in her rearview mirror. Her fear continued to grow. No matter what her eyes didn't see, she couldn't shake the feeling that there was a presence in the car with her and that it was evil. Very evil.

The young woman left Cape Cod by crossing the Sagamore Bridge. Suddenly, the supernatural presence left the car. For whatever reason, the spirit couldn't or wouldn't cross the Cape Cod Canal. It was as if the spirit jumped into the water so that it could remain on Cape Cod.

Since this incident, no one feels an evil presence in any part of the Scargo Café. It looks like Junior hasn't found his way back. Perhaps he's found another place to haunt.

But that doesn't mean that there aren't other ghosts at the café. Lights pop on and off without warning. Silverware moves from one table to another by unseen forces. Phones ring, but no one is on the other end. And sometimes an icy chill is felt near the lobby fireplace.

It's believed that this ghost is the original owner, Luther Hall, a Civil War soldier who built the home after the war. Luther was a busy man who liked to be useful. He managed his father-in-law's candy store, served as postmaster, and was a chairman of the Dennis school system. The incidents that happen at the Scargo Café aren't evil. Perhaps it's just Luther. And as in life, he's just trying to be helpful.

CHAPTER 9

Addie Keeps Watch

The manicured grounds and elegant mansion of the Ocean Edge Resort and Golf Club in Brewster are picture-perfect. It doesn't seem like anything bad could ever happen at this beautiful historic resort. But something bad did happen here over a hundred years ago. And now, one ghost is determined that nothing like that will ever happened again. This unofficial caretaker patrols the property to make certain that all are safe.

Brewster is a picturesque town on the north shore of the cape that looks out over Cape Cod Bay. It was settled in 1656 and officially became a town in 1803. It became known as the "sea captain's town" because more than fifty sea captains lived here during the eighteenth and nineteenth centuries.

Samuel Mayo Nickerson was born in Chatham in 1830. He traveled far and wide and eventually ended up in Chicago, where he

made his fortune working first in the liquor business and then in finance. Samuel, his wife, Matilda, and their only child, Roland, spent most of the year in Chicago, but Samuel loved Cape Cod so much that the family traveled there in the summer.

Roland was twenty-seven when he married Addie Daniels. Samuel usually gave his son anything he wanted, and now he wanted to do the same for his daughter-in-law. In the late 1880s, Samuel stood on a bluff in Brewster, looking out over Cape Cod Bay. He stuck his gold-tipped cane in the ground. He declared it the ideal location for a summer home for his son, daughter-in-law, and three grandchildren.

Fieldstone Hall was completed in 1890. The three-story wooden Victorian mansion included four chimneys, a balcony, a veranda, and covered porches. It sat on forty-eight acres and included a private beach, a pond, a nine-hole golf course, and a carriage house with a tower.

Taking care of the massive home and grounds required a staff of twenty-two servants. And they had to hire extra help when they entertained, which was often.

In spring of 1906, Fieldstone Hall burned to the ground. A fire started in the cellar and quickly spread throughout the wooden structure. Luckily, no one was injured, but the house and its contents were a total loss. Two weeks later, Roland Nickerson died from heart trouble, said to be brought on from the shock of the fire.

Addie rebuilt Fieldstone Hall with her father-in-law's help. They made the new home as fireproof as possible for an early-twentieth-century home. Reinforced steel and concrete were used in addition to four-foot-thick walls.

The second Fieldstone Hall was even grander than the first. It featured marble fireplaces, a massive staircase, and intricately carved oak woodwork. The billiard room was so large that the Nickerson children reportedly roller skated in it.

Several years after Addie's death in 1938, her family sold the home. It passed through several hands before it became the Ocean Edge Resort and Golf Club in 1986.

The supernatural activity that occurs, including lights turning on and off, is rumored to be due to Addie. In fact, anything out of the ordinary is blamed on Addie, from falling chandeliers to elevator doors that won't close. No one knows whether Roland or Samuel's ghosts remain on the property. If they do, they keep to themselves.

Before her death, Addie donated 1,727 acres to the state for a park in memory of her husband and a son who died in the 1918 flu epidemic. Nickerson State Park was the first state park in Massachusetts and remains popular with visitors today.

The Nickersons used this land as a private hunting reserve. Addie enjoyed hunting and was quite good at it. So if you visit Nickerson Park, keep watch for a woman astride a horse with a gun at her side.

The present management of the Ocean Edge Resort denies the that the property is haunted. But it does believe that Addie Nickerson is an important part of the history of the house. Pictures of the Nickerson family can be found throughout the main house, which now serves as a banquet, dining, and conference center.

If you do get a chance to stay at the Ocean Edge Resort and Golf Club, keep an eye out for Addie. And you can feel safe in the thought that she's keeping an eye out for you.

Three's Company

Ed and Laurie Maas got their first clue that all was not as it seemed right after they bought the foreclosed home from the bank. Townspeople began approaching them with alarm. "Are you crazy? The place is haunted!"

The six-story Victorian home in Orleans must once have been a grand place. But it had sat neglected for many years. Yet the couple saw the beauty in its structure and its potential.

They saw what it could be again as the Orleans Waterfront Inn.

Ed questioned the realtor, who mumbled something about rumors. When Ed did his own research, he found that the ghosts of this home, built in 1875, had been the subject of newspaper articles more than once.

Yet the family hadn't noticed anything strange, so they proceeded with their plans to renovate the property into a restaurant and inn. By the time the three ghosts decided to reveal themselves, the Maas family was attached to the house. Then they found themselves becoming attached to its ghostly residents.

The Maas family has identified the ghosts of three people, who all died tragically on the property. Details have been provided by visiting paranormal investigators. Although they don't know the actual names of the ghosts, the Maas family has given them names.

The two male spirits aren't very sociable. Fred, a one-time bartender, hangs out either in the belvedere on top of the house or in the restaurant. (A belvedere is a structure on top of a building that allows people to take in the view). Sadly, Fred committed suicide by hanging himself in the belvedere.

The Maas daughters and a few guests have observed glasses moving along the bar in the restaurant as if someone has pushed a glass to a customer. A guest and the paranormal investigators have both reported having ghostly encounters in the belvedere too.

The other male ghost is called Paul. He was once a dishwasher in the restaurant. He also stays close to where he died and where he worked. He committed suicide in the basement. His shadow continues to appear there on occasion. And then there's a door in the kitchen that slams shut occasionally. The kitchen staff believes Paul does this when the door has been open for too long.

The third ghost is the one who introduced herself first and is most active. The Maases named her Hannah after a member of the original family who lived here. However, Hannah wasn't part of the original family. She, like Fred and Paul, worked in the building. But unlike her ghost roommates, Hannah was murdered here.

Hannah first introduced herself to Laurie Maas. Laurie was showing a friend around the place a few weeks after they bought it. When Laurie and her friend reached the third floor, a frigid blast of air shot through the hallway. The air went through them. Laurie describes the experience as "a ghost seeking the warmth of their bodies."

Soon afterward, the Maas family discovered that Hannah enjoyed opening doors as well.

One night after they had purchased the property but before they moved in, Ed couldn't sleep and stopped by the house to check on it. Although he had put new locks on all the doors and locked up when he left that day, every door was standing open that night. He went inside and heard footsteps and voices upstairs. He suspected the intruders weren't of this world. If his visitors were supernatural, there wasn't much point in calling the police.

Ed left the house and went across the street to a convenience store. He sat and watched all night and never saw anyone leaving the house. With what he knows now, Ed suspects it was Hannah entertaining guests.

Hannah continues to enjoy leaving doors open, so the Maases have to watch for that. But Hannah also likes to relight candles in the dining area after they've been blown out. Sometimes staff will have to blow them out two or three times.

After the opening of the pub and dining room, Ed began doing more research on the house. He discovered that it was built by sea captain Aaron Snow, who descended from the area's earliest Pilgrims.

Because he was a sea captain, Snow added a two-story belvedere to the top so that his family could watch for his ship from the high perch overlooking Nauset Harbor and the Orleans town cove.

The Maas family heard a story of how Aaron's wife, Mary, would watch for his ship, the *Nettie M. Rogers*. Once the family spotted his ship, they would place a tree in the belvedere window as a welcome home message. The Maases so liked this story that they've put an artificial Christmas tree in the window, where it stays year-round. They want Aaron Snow know that he is always welcome at the Orleans Waterfront Inn.

When Aaron Snow built the home, the first floor was the town's general store. He, his wife, and their seven children lived upstairs. The devoted couple died within weeks of each other in 1892. There have been no signs of their ghosts.

The house sat empty for about eight years until two sisters, Clara and Emma, bought it in 1900. They operated it as a boardinghouse, but the sisters lived there as well, along with their many cats. When the Maases were having work done on the bedrooms, the workmen kept asking about the cats they could hear crying. The Maases had no pets. Soon after opening the inn to customers, a guest commented on the cats as well. Apparently, some of Clara and Emma's cats have had more than nine lives.

The next owners reportedly had criminal connections. They were rumored to be the Irish mafia. The time was during Prohibition. The house was the location for wild parties and illegal activities. It's believed that Hannah was connected to the house, and murdered there, during this period.

After World War II, the house became a luxury hotel where movie stars often stayed. But despite its popularity, a revolving

door of owners continued until the Maases purchased it in 1996. And they have celebrated twenty-five years of successful ownership.

The Maas family admits that they don't even notice the ghosts much anymore, but that ghostly activity happens in the Orleans Inn when you least expect it. But if you visit, ask the owners about the painting of the dancing ghosts—Hannah, Fred, and Paul!

CHAPTER 11

Hurried Haunting

It's not uncommon for hauntings and ghostly presences to be the result of something tragic. Perhaps the pain suffered in life or death keeps the spirit connected to this earth. Such is the case of the Truro tragedy, which has left Stephen Collins traveling a hilltop trail by horse for eternity.

Truro is located almost at the end of Cape Cod in an area called the Outer Cape. The view to the east is the Atlantic Ocean. To the west, look over Cape Cod Bay to Plymouth.

The Pilgrims stopped here briefly before sailing on to Plymouth. English colonists settled the area in the 1690s, and Truro officially became a town in 1709 and soon prospered. Fishing, whale hunting, and shipbuilding kept the people busy. They built homes and churches.

A hill called the Hill of Storms became the location for the first church, the First Congregational Parish of Truro, in 1709. The rectangular building that sits atop the hill now, built in 1827, is the third church in this location.

***

The bell tower holds an original Paul Revere Foundry bell. Because of this, it has been called the Bell Church.

It was dedicated to the "many brave seafarers and hardworking Cape Cod shipbuilders, chandlers, fishermen, farmers, merchants, and their families."

Stephen Collins oversaw the building of the first structure and was very dedicated to the church. He was an exhorter. This meant that although he hadn't been ordained a preacher, he could hold meetings and lead prayers. His role was to urge people to give their lives to the church. In Collins's mind, this meant that he had to be the first to arrive at the church, no matter what. The idea of being late caused him great anxiety.

At first, this compulsion harmed no one. Collins would just hurry up the hill on foot. But as he got older, walking up the steep hill became hard for him. So he purchased a gray mare. Being able to ride up the hill instead of walking didn't affect Collins's mood. He continued to be anxious about getting to the church before the congregation. The townspeople tried to tell him to slow down. But it didn't do any good. They soon learned to just stay out of his way.

Next to the church was a cemetery. Within it were tombstones of many male children, but the graves were empty. Truro was a seafaring community, and many people died at sea, their bodies never recovered. It was common practice for Truro boys to go to sea at the age of ten. Their young bodies were no match for rough seas, and many were tossed overboard by monstrous waves.

Silas Rich was one of those boys who went to sea. And he was one of the lucky ones who wasn't lost to the waves. At the age of ten, Silas began working on his father's fishing sloop. One day, a storm moved in and began pummeling the small ship. Silas's foot became tangled in the rigging. When the next wave hit, he was dragged overboard. Fortunately, his father was able to drag him back on board.

Silas suffered from a very bad blow to the head. He lost his memory, and he was unable to stand upright. Silas wasn't able to go to sea again, but he loved going to church. He liked listening to Stephen Collins preach, and the

exhorter always had something nice to say to the boy after services.

One Sunday, Collins seemed to be in a bigger hurry than ever to get to the church. He pushed his horse to go faster and faster. The horse struggled. Most people moved out of their way. But young Silas wasn't paying attention. He was mowed over by the horse and rider. The horse knocked over tombstones as well before they came to a stop at the church door.

Collins didn't seem to understand what had happened as he waited at the deacon's bench for the congregation to arrive. Two men carried in the trampled body of Silas Rich and laid him on the front bench. His parents wept silently. Collins stared at Silas's body throughout the service. At the end, he stopped and leaned over Silas for a minute. Then he left the church, never to enter it again.

On Sundays, Collins would stand outside

until the service was over and then go to the cemetery, where he would kneel for hours. Upon his death, the congregation buried him next to his beloved church.

People say that Stephen Collins's tortured spirit cannot rest. On the first Sunday of each month, parishioners say that the ghost of Stephen Collins appears riding a phantom horse. And if you listen carefully, you can hear the sounds of a horse's heavy breathing and the pounding of hooves.

The ghost dismounts at the church, walks to a worn gravestone, and kneels. The gravestones wear orange- and rust-colored lichen now. They are so worn that the names can no longer be seen. Whose tombstone does Stephen Collins kneel at? Is it Silas's grave or his own? We believe it is most likely Silas's grave that Collins mourns at. Perhaps if you visit, you'll see Collins and he will tell you.

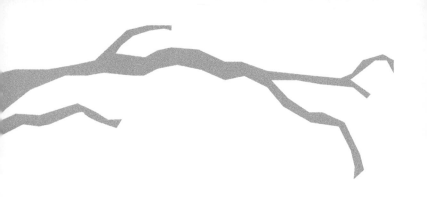

Conclusion

It is wonderful that five thousand years have now elapsed since the creation of the world, and still is undecided whether or not there has ever been an instance of the spirit of any person appearing after death. All argument is against it; but all belief is for it.

—Samuel Johnson

Samuel Johnson, an eighteenth-century poet and creator of the dictionary, has been celebrated as "the most distinguished man of letters in English history." And even he could not say for certain whether or not ghosts exist.

Over two hundred years after Samuel Johnson's quote was published, we are no closer to having a definitive answer. Do ghosts exist?

In search of an answer, we look to our own experiences and to the experiences of the people around us. As you can see from these Cape Cod ghost stories, some people are certain that the spirit sticks around after death under certain circumstances. Haunted tales provide us with a connection to the past. They give us hope by suggesting that perhaps death is not the end. Will there ever be a day when we know, without doubt, that spirits can slip back and forth between our world and theirs?

There will always be things we can't explain. And that's okay.

Karen Bush Gibson has written dozens of children's books on many different subjects. She writes about people, places, and history because she loves research. Gibson is a member of the Society of Children's Book Writers and Illustrators.

Check out some of the other Spooky America titles available now!

Spooky America was adapted from the creeptastic Haunted America series for adults. Haunted America explores historical haunts in cities and regions across America. Each book chronicles both the widely known and less-familiar history behind local ghosts and other unexplained mysteries. Here's more from *Haunted Cape Cod* author Barbara Sillery:

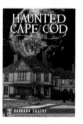